At the funf

I am at the fair. There is so much to see and do – flashing lights, crowds and good food smells!

Sam is keen to go on
The Big Dip. I am not!
It looks so high. I feel
sick just looking at it.

We go to the sweet shop
and get a box of popcorn.

Sam slips his hands in his pockets to get his cash out.

Oops! I lost my cash!

I get my cash out.

We go to The Room of Tricks.
I hand the man a ticket.

We go in. Sam looks thin
and I look short!

Next, we run to the clowns.
Sam drops the ping-pongs
in and wins!

Sam grins. He rips the top off the packet of gum. He chomps the lot.

I start to feel unwell.
"No need to stress, Dan,"
Sam tells me. "It will be fun."

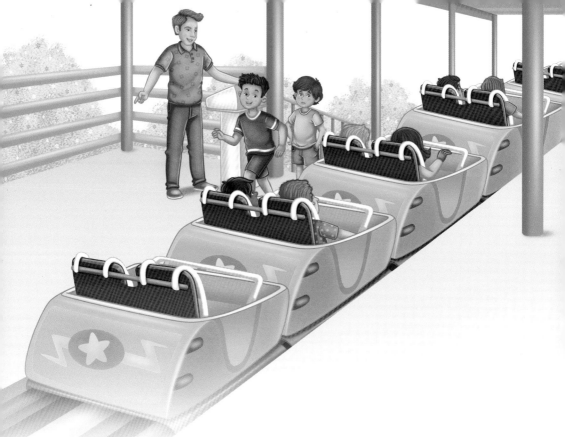

Sam and I go up the stairs
to the platform. We go right
to the back. Sam is glad.
I am not.

We sit down in a pair of chairs. The man shuts the bar and I grab on tight.

The train is going high
into the air. I look down.
Sam punches the air.

The Big Dip

We get to the top and then we are off!

The train speeds down and up, down and up. It twists and turns at high speed.

Then it ends and I am glad. We hop off.

That was so much fun, but I lost my gum!

No, it is stuck in my hair!

Words to blend

flashing	shop	crowds
food	keen	sweet
lights	cash	room
short	thin	start
tight	punches	speeds
platform	turns	high

Before reading

Synopsis: Dan and Sam have fun at the funfair. Sam wins a prize of gum then wants to go on The Big Dip. Dan isn't sure but Sam has a great time except he loses his gum.

Review phoneme/s: ar or ur ow oi ear

New phoneme: air

Story discussion: Look at the cover, and read the title together. Ask: *Have you been to a funfair like this? What kinds of things can you do at a funfair? What do you think will happen in the story?* Tell children that the story is written from Dan's point of view.

Link to prior learning: Display the trigraph *air*. Remind children that trigraphs are three letters that make one sound together. Can they read the trigraph *air* and say the sound? Point out that *air* is a word all on its own, but it also forms part of other words. How quickly can children find and read an *air* word on page 2? (*fair*)

Vocabulary check: Platform – a flat raised area you can stand on. Look at page 11. Can children point to the platform in the picture?

Decoding practice: Ask children to suggest words that rhyme with *air*. Write the ones that have the *air* spelling. (e.g. chair, fair, pair) Ask children to add dots under the single letter graphemes and dashes under digraphs and trigraphs, and sound out and blend each word.

Tricky word practice: Display the word *there*. Ask children to circle the tricky bit (the trigraph *ere*, which makes the sound /air/). Ask children to practise writing this word, and look out for it when reading.

After reading

Apply learning: Discuss the story. Can children explain what happened to Sam's gum? Ask: *Do you think Dan was brave to go on The Big Dip even though he was scared?*

Comprehension

- How does Dan help Sam out in this story?

- What prize does Sam win?

- Do you think Dan changes his mind about The Big Dip being scary?

Fluency

- Pick a page that most of the group read quite easily. Ask them to reread it with pace and expression. Model how to do this if necessary.

- Turn to page 13, and ask children to read the three sentences on this page with appropriate pace and expression, pausing for the full stops.

- Practise reading the words on page 17.

Tricky words review

so	are	do
go	we	of
no	my	out
have	me	be
was	there	you